C C
BIR. ____ .1AM

Ghost Stories

Prepare to be frightened by these terrifying tales from
around the Black Country & Birmingham

By

Brendan Hawthorne

Published by Bradwell Books
9 Orgreave Close Sheffield S13 9NP
Email: books@bradwellbooks.co.uk

British Library Cataloguing in Publication Data: a catalogue
record for this book is available from the British Library.

1st Edition

ISBN: 9781902674704

Print: Gomer Press, Llandysul, Ceredigion SA44 4JL
Design by: jenksdesign@yahoo.co.uk
Photograph Credits: Brendan Hawthorne, Sandwell
Community History & Archives Service
and The National Trust.
Illustrations by: Lauren Richards

Special thanks go to:

Staff at Sandwell MBC Museum Service,
The National Trust, Ian Bott and Lynn Hawthorne for
photographs, and all of the individuals who shared their
personal stories with me and allowed them to be gathered
within these pages. You know who you are!

Names have been changed or omitted where requested in order
to maintain the privacy of the individual concerned.

CONTENTS

INTRODUCTION

When asked to compile a series of ghost stories from the Black Country and Birmingham I was faced with a harsh choice. Should I go ahead and re-present the already well-known ghost stories of the region or research a book that contains new and personal stories of the unexplained?

That question was answered in less than a second! The pages that lie ahead of you contain tales and anecdotes from everyday people from all walks of life who have had an insight into what they believe to be the worlds of spirit. Invariably, their lives have not only been touched by the experience but for some, their lives have been significantly altered as a result of their encounters. It was also important for me to present stories from more modern times and not just tap the rich vein of material from the Victorian gothic. I have employed the use of face-to-face interviews, been given access to a fellow author's research notes and here and there, used old newspaper clippings as a source of information.

This little book will take you on a journey from mansion house to terraced house. It will take you from factory space to open space and prison cell to castle keep. Sit back, suspend your disbelief for a while and be aware of deep shadows and tricks of light! Come with me now and through these pages, we'll visit the places where people believe they have glimpsed the after-life and beyond!

Brendan Hawthorne

LADY BY THE LIGHT

On a pleasant August evening in 1956, a group of young people left a local dance hall in Tipton to walk home. Their humour was light-hearted after listening and dancing to old time favourites on a 78rpm player that replaced the usual dance bands on their nights off. Armed with their recent recordings and brimming with tired excitement the dancers began to disband into small groups. Usually a lift home was available to some of them depending on where they lived and more so if musicians had been playing at the venue. Hilarity often followed as people and instruments crammed into the cars for the short round robin drive home. Unfortunately no lifts were available on this particular evening. No one seemed to mind though as they were lifted on the warmth of late summer and the echoes of a favourite melody.

As the group approached Locarno Road one of the party would have to make her own way along the half-mile of houses and pubs to her home in Toll End Road. She was asked if she would be all right and as the time approached ten pm she assured the others that the regulars would be leaving The Harrier public house so she would be fine. She could always walk alongside a group of pub-goers for safety.

After saying their farewells twenty two year old Mavis made her way along the familiar route home. She was happy after a good night out and was thinking about the dances and the company of which she had been part.

The streetlights gave off a blue-white light as she walked along the rows of houses. Some living room lights were still switched on but the street seemed eerily quiet. As Mavis approached the open fields just before the cemetery she noticed a middle-aged couple making their way in the opposite direction. The gentleman parted company with the lady and went to walk across the fields as a short cut home, or as Mavis reminisced, it may have been to relieve himself of the after effects of a few pints! However, the lady, who was dressed in sombre clothing, in the blinking of an eye also mysteriously disappeared from view.

A couple of cars shushed along the road and a few people started to leave the pub shouting the usual merry *'good nights'* to each other. Sounds became eerily muted as Mavis looked across the road to where the lady had been standing a few moments earlier. It was then she realised that the woman who had disappeared so mysteriously had now returned.

Mavis's heart started to pound and her mouth became dry with fear and awe. She became paralysed and was seemingly rooted to the spot. A vision or apparition replaced the lady and was now floating three feet off the ground. Her clothing was illuminated bright white and had a pearly sheen to it. The light from her was so intense that the streetlights were dull by comparison. Mavis noticed that the lady was carrying a baby, a few months old. The child was wearing a shawl over its head and was carried in the crook of the lady's left arm. The child's clothes merged seamlessly into the drapes of the lady. Both appeared to have halos. Mavis tried to run but her feet were still firmly fixed to the pavement. She tried to call out but couldn't. She wanted to run to a nearby house but was overwhelmed by the entire beauty of the apparition. The vision held a calm gaze for a few moments. Mavis eventually managed to look away briefly to see if anyone else was witnessing what she was seeing. As she looked back the vision had gone and street-life sounds suddenly returned as people started to walk past her. Mavis ran to a nearby front garden gate, but what would the homeowners say if she told them her story? Instead she decided to run home, never once stopping until she reached the security of the entry-latch gate that led her to safety. She banged loudly on the back door. When her mother finally welcomed her in she said, "You look like you've seen a ghost," to which Mavis replied, "I think I probably have!"

The cemetery was reputed to have been haunted but this was no ordinary apparition. The vision and the sense that it gave Mavis have continued to bring comfort to her from that day to this. When she talks about this point in her life peace can still be seen to physically descend upon her.

These confrontations of spiritual visions are well documented but rare and often believed to be a good omen regarding fate and fortune to the individual. On this occasion alcohol cannot be used as an excuse. The dance hall only served tea and coffee!

ADDENDUM

On researching this story further there are other tales of similar events along that same stretch of road from Tipton to Ocker Hill. Back in Victorian times it's alleged that a lady named Margaret, reputed to be a 'Lady of the Night', found herself pregnant by one of her regulars. She is said by some to have died in childbirth. So you decide: mother or Madonna?

The awesome street light 'Madonna'

NO SELF-SERVICE AT THE HAUNTED BOOKSHOP

On a busy inter-section of the High Street in Wednesbury an unassuming row of shops curves along the well-trodden pavement of a small town thoroughfare. They are the usual mix of shops with a couple of 'old-tradition traders' standing resolute against the changes affecting most modern towns today. It is one of those shops to which the following relates.

Usually the bookshop doors opened onto the sardonic wit of the owner who would stand there behind his desk remonstrating the principle that he was destined for better things. The fact is, he loved his work but the comic tension always raised discussion and smiles. If times were good the shopper would also be greeted by the smell of a good cigar of which the owner would infrequently partake. On a bright sunny day the cocoon-like shop enveloped you in its timeless covers and multiplicity of titles. Rainy days, however, were best!

On one such day in the late 1990's a young man approached the bookshop owner with a view to renting one of the shop's upstairs rooms. This arrangement would be for a monthly meeting of like-minded people exploring the principles of what was then termed 'the new-age of spiritual enlightenment'.

Terms were set and advance rent paid to secure the agreed dates. The first few meetings successfully gained an interest and the attendees rose in number. Everyone commented on what a friendly atmosphere it was and how nice it was to meet up with other 'seekers'. One evening, however, was about to be the subject of a future meeting in its own right!

The site of the haunted bookshop and tea rooms

The scheduled evening meetings were often accompanied by rain so organisers of the event would wait in the shop, usually at the desk to the rear of the premises, to welcome participants and ensure dripping umbrellas and rain coats were placed in a suitable area as not to affect the stock of antiquarian and collectable books. On the night in question the rain-stained windows were rapidly becoming a kaleidoscope of colours with passing traffic and road lights. The effect gave a wonderful abstract veil from which to ascertain who would turn into the shop or continue on to whatever other business awaited them.

Time passed rather slowly and other than the two organisers no one else had turned up. After setting up the teas and coffees one of the organisers clomped down the steep stairs to see where everyone was. A couple of anxious glances went from one to the other as a strange scratching sound could be heard in the dimly-lit shop. The chief organiser said, "Blimey, I'll have to tell the owner about the mice he's got in here! Can you hear them?" The scratching stopped before re-starting and becoming louder in volume and scratchier in tone. "I heard that alright," said the assistant. "They must be big uns!" she added warily. The chief organiser nodded and said, "Or closer than we thought and more insistent!" A nervous laugh was exchanged to the accompanying scratching sound.

Suddenly the scratching stopped and was then exchanged for total silence. A look between the organisers suggested that they almost wished for the scratching to return as the shop became cold yet clammily oppressive. Just on it, a dragging noise was heard. "Do you see that?" whispered the chief organiser, "I don't believe it!" "What?" asked the assistant, "I can hear the noise but....." "Look at the bookshelf!" the chief organiser said abruptly, cutting across his colleague. Pointing shakily to a large volume of Victorian Home Care Hints it was plain to see that it was now removing itself from the line of books into which it was nestled so snugly only a few moments ago. Both people stood open mouthed as effortlessly the book reached its tipping point and fell to the floor with a large and dull thud! Immediately a small sphere of light shot from the vacant space and proceeded to fire itself around the walls like a fluorescent squash ball before disappearing back into the shelf.

"You did see that didn't you?" stammered the chief organiser. "I certainly did!" came the whispered, hoarse response.

The heat in the shop restored itself in seconds after the book was replaced on the shelf. Suddenly people started to arrive for the meeting, dripping wet from the heavy storm. The rest of the evening went ahead without a hitch.

Books that slide in the night

The following day the chief organiser returned the keys to the bookshop owner and told the story of the previous evening. The owner smiled broadly before the story was complete and said, "Have you had the book falling from the shelf? It's a common occurrence in here. You get used to all kinds of things happening. The rooms above the shops were once a tea room and it's believed one of the waiters still walks the floor looking to be of service!"

"Perhaps he didn't like the plastic cups!" quipped the organiser walking out of the shop.

THE OLD INSPECTOR CALLS BACK
FOR ONE LAST LOOK

Factories may be remembered as noisy, dirty and impersonal spaces however this was not the whole story. Those who worked in them would agree to some extent that they were definitely not conducive to the finer points of life but there was an irrepressible spirit that always filled these huge vacuous complexes with wit and humour.

One such place had traded in excess of a hundred and fifty years before it was finally closed down to relocate to cheaper foreign fields. It saw a lot of comedy and tragedy and many points in between. At night the old and rusting corrugated tin sheets would bang and rattle even if the evening air was still. It was as though the walls themselves were breathing, a living entity to the romantic. It was easy to imagine the worst when working alone where shadows were fleeting and reflections easily glimpsed in polished metal.

This story is not one from that environment. In fact, the day in question was bright and sunny. An early summer sun flooded in through the skylights dappling the shop floor with a soft golden light that illuminated metal dust on its rise and fall on circulating air currents. An electrician in his thirties was working at his bench making a wiring loom for the next vehicle to be fitted out.

The bench was one of four that were 'penned' off with grating from the rest of the fitting shop. Everyone, it seemed, was getting on with the tasks in hand. The pen had a heavy door that loudly banged shut on entry and exit so it was easy to detect whether anyone had entered into the space. Certainly no one could sneak up behind you without being heard.

The electrician suddenly sensed that he was being watched. He felt a cold chill extending to his fingers from his spine and soon realised that he was not alone. Whoever it was in his company was no longer of this world. As the electrician turned from the bench he was surprised to see an elderly gentleman, short in stature and stiff in nature, standing behind him. He was wearing a light brown cow-gown over black trousers and work boots. He also wore a white shirt and navy tie that was knotted and precise in shape and proportionate in size. He gazed intently at the workbench and the tangle of wiring that covered it. Making mental notes he began to appear lost, questioning and almost panicking. His steely eyes showed fear. The electrician turned to his bench to try and understand what was happening and what was upsetting this apparition so much. He turned back to the old fellow and asked if he needed any help. He noticed how lost he appeared to be and how his eyes pooled with such deep emotions. Gazing back towards his young friend the fellow gently smiled and softly and simply faded away. The electrician stood wondering what had just happened when a colleague breezed in and asked excitedly how long the old man had been turning up. The old inspector was just doing his duty, checking that standards were being maintained before he could be on his way, one last time.

A NEW HOME WITH OLD MEMORIES

Buying a new home can be traumatic enough with making sure everything is in place for the hand-over of keys and documents and getting over the setbacks of delayed completion times, ensuring the occupying vendor has finally left the building! One young couple couldn't wait to move into the old terraced property they had recently secured. The move had been troublesome as furniture had been in storage for a few weeks whilst new completion dates had been settled. Tea chest crates huddled in each of the rooms overflowing with packing material and potential but by the end of a long day the bed was in place, the sofa plumped up, the cooker connected, the hi-fi wired and the kettle on! They slept soundly that night and awoke to unpacking the contents of a one bedroom flat that seemed lost in the three-bedroomed property. The young man went up into the spare room to start on one of the tea chests as his partner was pegging out some washing. He could see her from the window that overlooked the garden they had so much wanted. All of a sudden the spare room was flooded with scent of violets. The smell was so heady that the young man's head spun. He looked around, no one was with him, and the box merely contained ornaments and fixtures. He rushed down stairs and out into the garden grabbing his partner's arm and telling her the story as they both ran into the spare room. The smell of old perfume had disappeared completely. Trying to save face he smelled the sleeve of his jumper, which still contained some of the smell of violets.

This incident was the start of a long sequence of events that took place over a few years. The smells continued with the homely aromas of roast lamb and apple pie cooking on returning home. From the garden the face of an elderly lady could regularly be seen looking out of the window. A small black dog was often encountered running down the stairs almost tripping up the new occupants. On re-decorating the kitchen, the young fellow before going to bed for a well-earned rest asked out loudly to the 'house' if what the couple were doing was ok. The next morning the kitchen had a line of 'correct' ticks on the newly-plastered wall drawn roughly in pencil. Cigar smoke could often be detected in the house of non-smokers. Apparently this was all to do with the old lady's husband who enjoyed a game of cards and a good Havana!

Over the years the young couple felt protected by this elderly couple that had seemingly not let go of the property. In fact from research it was ascertained by the owners that the old lady had a connection of over forty years with the property where many visitors saw her as a younger lady walking around the house in a summer's dress. One visitor, who was at the point of overstaying their welcome, decided to go to the toilet before they left for home. He left very quickly, white as a sheet, saying a ghostly woman had paid him a visit whilst he was paying a visit! The young couple, by chance met an ex childhood neighbour of the old lady. After some chat about the houses the young couple told their story of the family that still frequented the house. The neighbour told them that they had described to the last detail the lady, her husband and the black dog that accompanied them!

An old chimney sweep was called in one day to the property and as he walked into the kitchen he recounted the times he had visited this house before. Without prior knowledge the young couple had employed the same chimney sweep as the old lady had done thirty years before. He commented on the décor and how it looked and that everything was as he remembered apart from a sofa missing from by the back door. The only thing that was strange here was that between the old lady living there and the young couple moving in was a space of twenty-five years!

The young couple, now middle-aged, still live in the terraced house that is now a hundred and ten years old. In that time there have only been three owners and a few people who rented on short-term leases when it was first built, so happy is the house that continues to record all its happy memories.

The imposing Haden Hill House
Courtesy of Sandwell Museum Service

HADEN HILL HOUSE

Haden Hill House is a house of some history and benevolence that lies on the border between the borough's Sandwell and Dudley. It is open to the public and has had many a tale told about its hauntings dating back to the middle ages through to modern times.

The old hall was built in the late 1600's with the red brick Victorian pile being added in 1878. The buildings stand resplendent in fifty-five acres of parkland.

The following story occurred in the 1990's when an apartment within the property could be hired on short-term lets. Two single men in their twenties were looking to share a let whilst they were looking for their own accommodation when they learned that the Haden Hill apartment had become vacant. With great excitement they told everyone that the application had been successful and on the handover of keys one of the new occupants invited his sister over to look at the flat. His sister's partner had worked in the psychic and spirit 'field' and was asked what he 'felt' from the rooms. The following is a description taken directly from that evening by the two visitors.

SHARING A FLAT

'The rooms immediately began to envelop you, closing you in in a very oppressive way.'

'The rooms seemed to have eyes and you were made to feel quite unwelcome.'

During the visit a television set flickered in the corner of the living room and every so often the picture would break into the familiar static snow pattern. Suddenly people who weren't anything to do with the programme would be seen to walk across the screen like a shadow. At that moment the lady of the group decided to go to the toilet that was at the end of a long corridor. Her partner thought she was returning but when he looked again the lady he saw was smaller in stature and was wearing a Victorian maid's uniform and was carrying a tray. A few minutes later the lady of the group re-joined the party and told how the

Adding an extra dimension to your TV package!

temperature had suddenly dropped at that end of the property and for a few moments was seemingly locked in to the toilet.

As they walked through the property each room was unveiled and it was clear the two bedrooms contained some paranormal activity. One was a lot worse in feeling than the other and the psychic in the group commented on the fact that they wouldn't get much sleep in this flat as it was 'noisy' in a ghostly fashion. We will now take the story from each of the perspectives of the tenants.

John had the room that felt more intensely active. For the first week he was woken up every night by a tapping noise. At first he thought it was the wind blowing through the gaps in the windows. One night, however, the sound became more insistent and as he looked towards the window he could see the cords from the blinds being pulled and sent back, creating the tapping sound. From the way the cords were being 'pulled' it could be seen that this was no act of draughts playing on string. Something, someone, was creating this phenomenon. As the weeks progressed the tapping sound became incessantly familiar and eventually became an accepted part of the house until one evening things changed for the worse. John awoke to a dragging noise. It was intermittent at first then became more prolonged in duration. Startled he put his bedside lamp on expecting to see an intruder. He was stunned to see that his bag of diving weights was being dragged with some degree of effort across the floor by an unseen force!

Steve was constantly being awoken in the early hours by the hollow sound of tables and chairs being dragged around in the café area below his room. Both tenants would hear this sound and both of them would go to the café below to see that nothing had been moved. These occurrences got so bad that Steve would have to play CD's through his ear pieces all night so that the sounds couldn't be heard. This worked to some degree though at the main points of disturbance the clattering was still audible from below. It was as if the noise could penetrate through most diversions. The climax of happenings occurred at the beginning of December when suddenly a choir could be heard singing a requiem mass. This repeated itself every night for a week. After some investigation it was found that a requiem mass had been held in that month for one of the owners of the property during the Victorian period.

Standing in the shadows of Haden Hill House
Courtesy of Sandwell Museum Service

This last event proved too much for the two friends who hastily left the handy let and joined the long list of others who had foregone their commitment on the lease.

There are further stories regarding Haden Hill House regularly told by visitors.

The stories are often rooted on the servants' staircase and passageway that leads to the Learning Area and the offices where the daily routines of administration and management of the property take place. Another hot spot in the property is the main visitor staircase that lies to one side of the adjoining wall to the old part of the house. If we separate out the noises of scurrying squirrels and creaking boards we are left with some 'unexplainable happenings.' Here are a few of them.

TALES OF THREE STAIRCASES

Several parents of children have reported ghostly sightings and apparitions. These accounts are similar in nature and not connected. They have all occurred over a period of many years yet the same stories keep coming in.

One report came from a mother of a young child who had very matter-of-factly described seeing a lady, who was wearing an 'old costume', dancing at the top of the servants' staircase.
Another child refused to walk any further up the servant's staircase as a man was standing on the landing, looking stern and unwelcoming.

A parent carrying a young child-in-arms walked up the servants' staircase when the child started crying and screaming and didn't want their parent to walk any further. A member of staff helpfully advised the parent to walk with them and to use the main staircase to meet up with the same point of the tour of the mansion. As soon as the parent moved away from the servants' staircase the child stopped crying. They walked through the house and up the main staircase to the point where the servants' staircase connected with the main transit corridor on the upper floor. As they approached the point where the child had previously refused to go any further the child started to cry and scream again. As soon as the parents moved away from the point the child calmed down and became contented once more.

Staff at the property have regularly reported things going missing from that area of the house only to re-appear somewhere totally disconnected from where they were taken. It is with reports of this physical presence we move to the stairs leading to the attic from the servants' area.

The property regularly holds family fun days and a young visitor reported to a member of staff that a man had been seen going past the no-entry signs on the staircase leading to the attic door. The attic door was kept locked and staff have admitted that they don't like to go there alone. The member of staff thanked the visiting girl and spoke to some other people who had seen the man walk past them and through into the prohibited area. They had not seen the man return and as they had been standing on the stairs for the whole time the man could not have walked past them. The member of staff ascended the stairs and was ready to ask the man to return to the rest of the house. When she got to the top of the stairs there was no-one there. The man had completely vanished. It is at this juncture that a new story begins.

Another member of staff walked bravely to the attic door alone and went to walk into the room. She had unlocked the door earlier and had no reason to believe that there would be any problems with leaving the door unlocked whilst carrying out the duties. She pushed the door but it would not open. Thinking she may have just locked the door herself she put the key into the lock and found the door to still be unlocked. She tried the door again; rattling the door in the frame she was suddenly aware of a chilling draught that poured itself from under the door and rose in front of her like a curtain of ice. She felt the hairs on the back of her neck rise and at this point she decided to leave the door alone and went back to the offices shaken and looking very pale. Half an hour later she plucked up the courage to return to the attic door with a colleague. The door opened easily and the temperature had returned to normal.

Over to the main visitor staircase and a lady who was visiting the property reported hearing a quarrel next door. She said she could hear very clearly through the wall a man and a woman arguing. She asked which room lay beyond the staircase wall and could someone go and sort out the couple that was clearly and publicly having some major disagreement. A member of staff asked if she could be taken to the spot where the visitor had heard the argument taking place. It was here the visitor was told that behind the wall lay the old part of the property that was locked, empty and with no-one in there!

TALKING POINT

As described earlier Haden Hill House stands in substantial parklands that really are very beautiful. One fine summer's evening as twilight approached a new member of staff decided to take a break before facing the tiring journey home. It was a quiet evening except for birdsong. Clouds were migrating across the skies towards evening and the sound of gentle breezes stirred through the trees as the sun lost its remaining grip on the horizon. The staff member came abruptly back to his senses when he saw a man approaching him. The man was dressed in smart, dark clothing of a bygone age. He was reading from a book and then talking out loud. Not wanting to appear rude the member of staff gave the look 'I'm here to help.' In response the man gazed back for a moment. He then asked the member of staff if he believed in God and did he think children were turning away from God and religion? Trying not to get drawn in to a deep and potentially contentious conversation on such a beautiful evening the staff member skirted around the conversation until, surprisingly, another man joined them from the direction of the house. Turning to him the staff member was told by the new visitor to ignore the other man and was advised that he would go soon. The staff member smiled gently and as he turned to the first visitor he saw that he had completely vanished. He then turned back to the second visitor to get an explanation as to what was going on only to find that he had vanished as well.

On returning to the property the staff member was trying to make sense of what had just happened to him. As he walked through the house he came across some old family pictures that had recently been mounted on the walls in one of the corridors. The pictures were not generally known about and there was no way that he could have seen them before his excursion into the grounds. He stopped and checked that what he was seeing was correct. He was shocked to find that the two men he had been talking to were in fact past family members of the property's lineage and were long since dead. They must have simply been out for a walk on a beautiful summer night wanting to share their theories with all!

ELEANOR AND THE MONK

A well-known story of the parklands at Haden Hill is that of Eleanor and the monk. Eleanor was a woman from a nearby village who fell in love with a monk from Halesowen Abbey. The monk was allegedly bricked into a wall in the Abbey. His accusers bricked him into a void leaving one brick out to view what was left of his world. Through this same window he would be fed until such time came as his punishment was deemed to be over or indeed escalated. The only fresh air the monk would get was from through this same missing brick. He was fed infrequently on bread and water and was given a candle with which to light his darkest hours. In this cramped and confined space he languished for an indeterminable amount of time before the final brick was eventually put in place. This was to seal the fate of a man found guilty of loving a woman. To his accusers the crime was punishable by a slow and uneasy death, having gone against the vows of his order. Eleanor is said to walk the grounds of Haden Hill still in mourning over the loss of her only love.

The old Oak House of Tudor yeoman's stock
Courtesy of Sandwell Museum Service

BRIEF TALES FROM THE HOUSE OF OAK

We now move to the outskirts of the town of West Bromwich. Here we find a beautiful late Tudor property hidden in the middle of a huge area of terraced and semi-detached properties dating from Edwardian times to the 1930's.

The original owners of this fine 'yeoman's house' are not known. The Turton family were possibly the earliest recorded owners in the 1630's. The Whyley family took over the property from 1768 to1837. The house then passed through many hands until the benefactor Alderman Farley took ownership with the intention of making Oak House his residence. However, he decided to turn the building into a museum and presented the restored property to the people of the town in July 1898 and in whose hands it remains to this day. The Oak House derives its name from the huge oak tree that stood nearby and was destroyed by fire in the early 1800's.

FEELING AT HOME

The most atmospheric room at Oak House is arguably the dining room. It has fine period detail and furniture and is where clocks can often be heard ticking and chiming. The chilling part of this is that none of the clocks actually work! It is in this room that the occurrence of smelling sweet smelling pipe tobacco takes place. It is a fairly infrequent smell, although it did present itself to the visiting Mayor of the French town with which West Bromwich is twinned. As a member of staff walked him round he commented on the smell of fresh pipe tobacco. He had not been told of the ghostly goings on at this point!

The stairs at Oak House creak and groan like many other properties of its ilk and age. However, when footsteps are accompanied by flashes of green costumes and children disappearing into walls next to fireplaces many visitors can be excused for thinking that they are possibly seeing something of life that took place during the times of the original floor plan to the property.

It is on this staircase where one volunteer sensed the overwhelming emotion of longing for a lost love accompanied by the vision of a lady looking through the side window and out across the grounds at the rear of the property. Maybe she still

The main staircase at The Oak House
Courtesy of Sandwell Museum Service

waits for her love to return, her memory fuelled by the accompanying smell of fresh, sweet pipe tobacco.

It is a simple wooden staircase that leads directly to the front bedroom at Oak House. This area of the property is said to be the most active part of the house for unexplained reports and 'goings on'. One day a volunteer was lightly dusting some of the furniture in the front bedroom. The only other member of staff who was on duty that day had gone to collect the living history costumes from the local laundrette in readiness for the new term. The volunteer was now alone and happily working away, content in her surroundings. Out of the corner of her eye she saw a figure walk across the doorway as if contemplating whether or not to enter the bedroom. She thought nothing of it and assumed that the figure was her colleague returning to the building having forgotten something. She carried on with her work and again became aware of the same figure walking across the doorway. The volunteer stopped what she was doing and checked every room for the visitor. She discovered that there was no-one else in the house of this world other than herself and on resuming her work she kept a keen and watchful eye on the doorway until her colleague returned.

THE MANOR HOUSE

The old Manor House is situated on the borders of Wednesbury and West Bromwich and dates back to the1270's. It is a fantastically well-preserved timber beamed property having had extensions built during the 15th and 16th centuries. For a time, through the 1970's to the 1990's, it was leased to a brewery and operated as a pub/restaurant. During this time the building was

The Old Manor House- host to ghosts and apparitions?

extended again to enhance its new commercial function and began trading on the lure of a Tudor-beathan look banqueting hall. After the pub closed the building fell into some disrepair until the use of the building retuned to the local council. The Manor is currently part of the museum service in Sandwell.

THE VIGIL

In the 1980's a new group of would-be parapsychologists were to cut their teeth on what is now called a vigil. They went to the Manor armed with tape recorders where they set about recording background noises to test otherworldly sounds against.

They recorded themselves breathing, walking and talking as well as the sounds from the nearby road. As darkness descended they were ready with their near to scientific regime of listening in ready to connect with the other side.

Throughout the night many bumps and groans were heard as the house settled into slumber. The night gave way to early hours in a truly unremarkable fashion. The strain was beginning to tell as slow hour passed into slow hour. One of the group started to read and as they did so she felt her nose go cold. She remarked to the tape recorder what was going on and then felt nothing more. Daybreak came and the tired team packed away the recorders and headed for home and a well-earned sleep. A few days later the tapes were edited down into sounds categorised as 'explainables' and 'unexplainables'. The unexplainable tape lasted for less than thirty seconds. It contained the sound of children playing on the lawns outside the Manor. The time clock would have put that at around four am! Then, of course, there was the cold nose incident. You could clearly hear the team member say that their nose was cold. What no-one had heard before was the ghostly voice of a child saying 'I know that' and then laughing loudly!

NEVER WORK WITH....

More recently another group of parapsychologists conducted a vigil in the Manor House. One area of the building is known by staff for very specific types of activity but these were not conveyed to the team of investigators.

The South Solar regularly bears witness to a cat appearing and disappearing.

A sensation that many people feel at the property is the gentle rubbing of a cat on their legs. When they look down there is no

Getting a helping hand on a busy day

cat around them! Reported sightings of the cat match with that of one of the pub's old cats now long since dead to this world. Another regular incidence at the Manor is that of footsteps on the stairs often accompanied by sightings of a boy and girl sitting on or climbing the staircase.

ROLL UP! ROLL UP!

There are guided tours to be had around the Manor House and usually the guide will talk about the history and the rooms but one day one guide had a little more to contend with. As she gathered the next group of people together she stood in close proximity to the 1960's extension in a small courtyard area. The guide went through her usual opening to the tour welcoming all the property and giving a little background before moving off and taking the party around the grounds. Suddenly she was aware of someone or something gently brushing her neck. At first she thought it may have been her clothing and gently ran her hand round to feel if anything was causing the sensation. There was nothing there to cause it so she dismissed it until it came again and again! She then felt two hands press firmly on her shoulders. She tried hard not to show her emotions to the listening public. It wasn't until after the tour and she managed to get to the main hall did she finally come to terms with the sensations she had felt. Clearly pale, her manager asked if she had seen a ghost. She replied that she hadn't seen a ghost, merely felt the presence of one close by!

WHO'S THE FAIREST....?

Hallowe'en is always the high point of any old building wanting to put on a safe spectacle for the public. The heightened awareness and expectations of the time of year add to the whole excitement of conjuring demons, ghosts and witches from beyond the thin veil that differentiates spirit from physical worlds.

Again in the pub part of the building at the Manor one volunteer was applying make up in the bar mirror. The ghoulish make up was going on well and she was preparing to get into character for the night ahead. Usually touring parties of members of the public would be guided around waiting to be

Someone else in the frame?

scared, made uneasy and then be able to laugh at the suspense as it ebbed and flowed. Unfortunately for this volunteer the veil between this world and the next got a little bit too thin and there beside her reflection in the mirror was the reflection of another face staring passively at her. As she regained her composure and focus she turned around to find that no-one was there to cast the reflection. She turned back to the mirror and caught in her peripheral vision the reflection moving away to leave her own partially made up face staring back at her.

THE BARMAN WITH AN UNDERSTANDING EAR

This next story is probably a generic story and can be told in most bars but is still worthy of a mention. One man who was going through some personal domestic problems started to frequent a pub that was new to him. He wanted to avoid his old mates and the regulars at his local haunt as he didn't want to have to answer any awkward questions.

Every night he would go to the bar to the same barman who he felt could give him a sympathetic ear. Over the weeks he divulged quite a lot of personal information. The barman always smiled and nodded in the right place and offered what seemed to be sound and common sense advice, so much so that the customer managed to get things sorted out with his wife and headed off divorce proceedings.

The customer thought he should go into the pub and thank the barman personally for 'being there' and helping him sort through this troubled time in his life.

On entering the pub another barman was standing in the place of his new friend. The customer asked where he could find the tall thin man with a receding hairline, the one in the white shirt and grey waistcoat who always had a smile. The barman in front of him paled and said, "You mean Jim? He died years ago mate but he does return from time to time for those in need of his reasoning."

THE OLD FOUNDRYMAN'S TEA TIME RETURN

Tower Street in Dudley has seen some changes over the years. The street formed a hill and was also elevated on one side so that properties on the hill had steps leading up to them from the pavement. In the early 1980's two portacabins stood there on a rough piece of demolition land owned by the council. It offered some car parking to the office staff that worked from the temporary additional office space, the staff there often getting a shock when the nearby fire station would test its sirens as part of its daily routines! One member of staff who owned a very leaky old mini car asked for help when she found six inches of water in the foot-wells after a torrential downpour. One of the fire crew asked if they should pump the water out or merely pick the car up, tip it upside down and shake it! The former was seen as the best bet!

So there it was, a working environment on the edge of town where everyone got along playing their part in the community. It is this strong sense of identity that brings us this next story. The office staff was made up of an all female workforce who had to cover telephone enquiries from eight in the morning to

The now derelict Tower Street site formerly terraced houses and later temporary offices

six in the evening. This meant some ladies started early and finished earlier. Others started late and finished later. One lady who was left to lock up most frequently at night suddenly became aware that she wasn't always as alone as she thought she was.

Sitting at her desk at just gone six one evening she heard the sound of heavy footsteps on the staircase leading to the office. The footsteps were those of a man and were probably caused by work boots. The stairs consisted of half a dozen boarded steps on a hollow framework so easily worked as an early warning sign for approaching visitors to the office. She looked at her watch. She asked herself who could be visiting at this late a stage in the day. She then thought of personal safety. The neighbouring office was empty and the outer door unlocked. Her pulse raced a little and her mouth became dry at the prospect of an intruder. What should she do? She waited for the door to open, ready to give whoever a what-for for spooking her so much. No-one arrived and no-one had left. There were no further sounds that evening. However, this occurrence repeated itself night after night. Members of staff stayed later to witness it. No-one could explain the footsteps that led up the stairs and then stopped.

A few months later a member of staff was in the information office in the town and found an old postcard of Tower Street from the 1910's. It showed a row of terraced houses where the offices now stood. They had the equivalent number of stone steps leading to the front door. The photograph was placed in the office and the footsteps ceased to be heard from that day forward. Maybe the sound of footsteps was an old foundry-man coming home for his tea dragging his tired legs those last few steps home. All he needed was a bit of recognition and warm welcome home!

WHO'S THERE AT THE VICTORIAN MANOR?

A Victorian manor house in Wolverhampton is the location for our next story. It is open to the public most days but before and after closing times the house is left to rest as the office staff continue to work into early evening.

Two female members of staff were working late. All of the outer doors were closed and locked for security and no-one else was in the building.

Wightwick Manor- home to a noisy staircase and impromptu light shows
Reproduced courtesy of The National Trust

The offices are included in a suite of rooms on the first floor off the old servants' staircase. The stairs are uncarpeted.

The two members of staff were both alerted to someone walking up the stairs. They had not heard the outer door open and close with its usual collection of creaks, groans and bangs. The footsteps, however, were of someone running and as they reached the top landing they stopped. Up until this point reports of hearing people whispering to each other in the servants area had been reported and the images of a lady dressed for dinner at another point in the property. The footsteps, however, were new.

Startled, the two ladies ventured towards the closed, wooden office door. One member of staff armed herself with the first thing that came to hand. Unfortunately, it was a cardboard tube that had protected a poster in the mail system!

They opened the door to no-one. Bravely, they decided to check on the rest of the property for intruders and for security reasons. As they reached the downstairs main room they cautiously switched on the electric lights expecting the perpetrator to be bought to book. The lights, however, suddenly flared up and then dimmed several times. They heard the doors of other rooms opening and closing until suddenly, without fuss, everything stopped. The lights went back to normal and the noises ceased. No-one else apart from the two members of staff were found to be in the property that evening. Explanations have been offered but none have definitively answered all of the issues raised. Sightings of a woman waiting to go to dinner are still reported from time to time and whispers can still be heard along

The servants' staircase at Wightwick Manor
Reproduced courtesy of The National Trust

corridors when the property is closed. Perhaps the upstairs and downstairs of life still continues along these corridors of power, benevolence and intrigue!

BE GOOD FOR YOUR MOM

In 1970 the witness to the following story was four years old. Her friend, of similar age, lived a few doors away and over the years they would become firm childhood pals.

The witness's friend had a father who had been ill for a number of years. Through all of his personal discomfort he would do his best to support his young daughter. Bringing his daughter up with good manners and good behaviour was most important to him. However, one particular day in this young girl's life would become a moral blueprint that would last a lifetime.

Reminiscing, she remembers the day when a lot of people seemed to be visiting the house. She was kept away from the new visitors whom she really wanted to meet and couldn't understand why so many people were in her house. She glimpsed them out of the window. She heard them moving things around the house and at one point thought she heard someone crying but couldn't be certain.

Bedtime came along and the usual regime was restored before she finally settled down to sleep. A few hours later she awoke. The house was quiet and she needed to get up to go to the toilet. As she left her room and walked across the landing she saw her father at the top of the stairs. He stood there in his pyjamas and giving her his usual smile he said in his calm voice, "Go back to bed and be good for your mom." She turned, went back to bed and fell asleep straight away.

Next day she asked her mom where her dad was as she had seen him during the night on the landing. It was then she was told that her father had passed away the day before so she couldn't have possibly seen him in the early hours of the morning.

The visitors to the house had been the various authorities and organisations needed in times of someone passing away. Even now, as an adult, she finds it comforting that her father had spared the time to say, in his own way, 'Goodbye.'

THERE'S NO SMOKE

We're back to the Haden Hill area for this next story of the unexplained. A house that backed onto the grounds of Haden Hill House belonged to a young, active, non smoking and down-to-earth local family.

One day the family's youngest son, who was ten years of age at the time of these events, started to complain about his bedroom having the strange smell of a lit cigarette to it and that he didn't want to go to bed because of it. Unusually, this smell only became apparent in the middle of the night and was accompanied by the vision of someone sitting at the foot of the bed. When the visitations took place the son would often need comforting by going into his parents' room. These incidences began to disrupt the whole family, so much so that one night the child's father said that he would sleep in his son's room to

No smoking in the house please!

experience it for himself. He would find out who he was and put an end to it once and for all.

That night the father slept soundly, though guarded as to what he might encounter on this challenge to disprove his son's story. All he wanted was to get things back to normal and just get a good night's sleep.

In the darkest hour the father roused from his deep sleep. He was aware of a strong odour that very quickly drew him to his senses. He could smell high tar tobacco that was now filling his nostrils and lungs to almost acrid irritation. Coughing, with eyes watering and sensing a growing feeling of dread and fear, he sat upright and immediately felt the weight of someone sitting at the foot of the bed. He looked along the length of the bed and saw the hunched figure of an old man smoking and looking at his watch. As his son had said he was looking at someone, apparently waiting. Waiting for what?

Within a short space of time the vision simply melted away and with it the overpowering smell of nicotine and tar.

The next morning the family sat around the breakfast table as the father regaled the story from the night before. The son looked relieved at the fact he was now not only believed but also being taken seriously. They obviously felt they had a problem but to whom should they turn?

Eventually, the father decided to get the local vicar in to splash holy water and to say a prayer to the deliver the spirit safely to the shores of the afterlife. Unfortunately, the exorcism didn't work and the son continued to see the old man smoking and waiting at the foot of his bed in the middle of the night.

A medium from the local spiritualist church was called in next to see if she could shed further light on the disturbing situation. Immediately she walked through the door she reported to the family that the vision was nothing to do with the family at all. She then went on to say the man was merely waiting for his friend and that he wouldn't have to wait much longer. The family asked for whom was he waiting. The medium replied that he was waiting for the man next door. They were long time friends and as soon as the neighbour passed away they would have no more issues with the smoking man. On that she left.

The neighbour, a fit and healthy man, obviously wasn't told of the situation. What could the family do now? Ten days later came the news that the neighbour had collapsed and died suddenly, without prior warning or illness. From that day things returned to normal for the family. The man at the foot of the bed had waited for his friend, smoked a few cigarettes along the way and remained loyal to the foretold needs of an old mate.

AN OLD SOLDIER'S RETURN

The old Royal Hospital in Wolverhampton finally closed its wards in June 1997. It had changed its identity over many years, initially being founded as the Wolverhampton Dispensary in 1821 for servicing the health needs of the poor. During the mid-nineteenth century it was deemed no longer fit to service the demands of the area. The building and its contents went through a series of improvements and in changing to The South Staffordshire General Hospital and Dispensary, eventually offered eighty beds for adults. It saw its fair share of disaster and trauma with colliery accidents and the onset of The Great War when thirty beds were offered to the Red Cross for wounded soldiers.

When the hospital was in decline some of the old corridors and wards would eventually give up their ghosts. Staff would be subjected to the sounds of moaning and groaning from empty sections of the hospital. On occasion old soldiers have been see in bloody bandages and field dressings waiting to be relieved of their pain by these dutiful nurses. It would appear that their stories were still being recounted on an endless loop of professional conscience during difficult personal times.

It is from this point that this story begins. There have been many reports of the ubiquitous Grey Lady visions that seem to accompany most so-called haunted buildings. However, this grey lady could easily be recognised as a nurse walking the wards. One nurse who worked at the hospital in the 1990's regularly saw nurses in 'old uniforms' walking along corridors and around the reputedly haunted operating theatre. The strange thing was that the apparitions of the nurses could not be seen below their knees but were still going about their daily routines with an air of duty and purpose. It was later discovered that the area where these nurses were walking had been subject to a change in floor level. The raising of the floor was calculated as being equivalent to the approximate length of foot to knee!

The next two stories come from Selly Oak in Birmingham. The stories were gleaned from an ex-police officer during a chat over a mug of tea! We go back to the 1990's for our next excursions into the unknown.

The crossroads at Selly Oak Park

A WALK IN THE PARK

Twenty odd years ago a young police officer was given the job of walking the police dogs across Selly Oak Park as it was closest to the police station. The walks often took place late at night or in the early morning before or after a shift. The park itself was welcoming and had three well-lit paths that led to the central point of the park which was lit by a street lamp-style light and the obligatory waste bin!

The paths themselves were leafy and tree-lined and were the object of many a dog on the scent of something interesting and whatever dogs do against trees. This area drew dog walkers of every description to the meeting point where the regulars held many a conversation both canine and human. However on some occasions, how shall I say, there were other elements at work!

One evening the police officer was out walking two young police dogs. They were boisterous and playful and thankful of their free time. Suddenly, and from nowhere, an elderly man was seen walking towards the dogs. He was carrying a walking stick and wore a flat cap and dark overcoat over dark trousers and polished shoes. A light mist was just staring to form on the chilly night air but visibility was still excellent. Drifting on the air currents the elderly man could be heard whistling a tune. It was

I was just walking the dogs when.......

a timeless sort of tune, one from a long time ago, melancholic but strangely familiar to the young officer. Snapping from the momentary trance that he had fallen into he called the dogs to heel. They came running obediently and were quickly on their respective leashes. The police officer didn't want the elderly gentleman to be startled by two playful police pups so he stepped off the path and into the tree line where he waited for the old man to pass under the lighting. The whistling got louder and louder as he approached and at the point where he would have seen the man and was ready to bid him goodnight the whistling stopped abruptly. The elderly gentleman never walked past. In fact, he had simply vanished into thin air.

DEAD CENTRE

The next sequence of events took place over several weeks and was experienced by several witnesses. At the central point of Selly Oak Park the same police officer and his colleagues discovered a circular cold area. Even on a summer's night this spot was not just cold, it was freezing. The officers actually traced the area on a local map and demonstrated the phenomenon to friends and colleagues much to the mystification of all. In turn they would breathe out and no breath could be seen. They would then step inside the circle and breath could be visibly seen expiring from their chilled bodies! When walking the police dogs in this area the dogs would simultaneously turn and fix their eyes on the same spot and would growl for no visible reason.

Selly Oak Park- A policeman's beat

One warm July evening, whilst off duty, our intrepid officer walked to the dead centre of the park, entertaining the idea of stepping in and out of the area to watch his breath appearing and disappearing when he walked in and out of the circle. He recalls almost panting like his dogs such was the fervor he felt in relation to this strange happening. Well, he must have upset somebody on the other side with his playful attempt at trying to work out what was happening. He describes 'an unseen hand' forcibly pushing him backwards from the centre point so hard that he fell several feet backwards on his derriere. 'Did this put the wind up him?' I asked him. He looked pensive and countered, "All the way home! I never went back there again.

In fact I moved away altogether! I'm still told though that some locals still find that part of the park to be very 'odd' on certain nights."

NEW BEGINNINGS

Our next story takes us back into Birmingham where a lady who had been divorced a few years earlier meets up with a new partner and after some time of courtship they decide to live together before going down the marital aisle.

Her new partner was the youngest of two sons, their mother having died some five years previously. With her final breath she had said that she would not and could not rest until her last son was married.

The lady, whom for this story we shall call Susan, moved in with her husband to be (John) in the home where he had lived with his mother. This was a temporary arrangement whilst they saved their money and renovated a new property for when they were finally married. Susan soon discovered that her mother-in-law's house had been left pretty much as it had been the day she had been taken into hospital. Susan took on the task of clearing out the clothes and personal effects of her late mother-in-law out of a sense of duty to both her new partner and the lady whose house she now inhabited.

As Susan sorted through the personal belongings she came across a letter that had been sent during the Second World War. It was from John's father and was a letter like many that had been sent during those uncertain years of soldiers wondering if they would ever see home again. From the letter it was obvious that the wartime couple were expecting their first child. The words of the letter resonated with Susan as they went on to illustrate the fears of a young soldier who said that he wanted his son to know that he loved him and he longed to see the day when his son could run along their front garden path to welcome his dad home from the atrocities of war. Suddenly Susan found herself crying at the sadness within the letter then felt like she was being held in someone's arms. She felt the love of her mother-in law surround her as she cradled her in her arms and was comforted by the experience. She knew her mother-in-law was with her from that moment on in spirit. Susan had always felt that she may not have been seen as acceptable for this lady's son as she had been married before and now she was living with her son out of wedlock! As the days went on and the tidying out continued, so did the confirmation of acceptance. Whilst going through some clothing and cleaning up the bedroom one day, Susan heard a voice say, ' Go on, go on and ask him about the lawn mower and why I hit him with a broom.' Susan wondered why on earth such a specific thing would come to mind from something of which she knew nothing. Later that day Susan asked John what this phrase meant and told him how she had come by it. John physically paled. Susan went on to explain that she had heard a woman's voice in the bedroom telling her to ask him. John started to laugh and explained how he had been out the night before the day in question and drunk several pints of beer and was feeling the worst for wear the following day. His mother had asked him the day before to get up early and mow the lawn for her but that had obviously not happened. John got up much later than intended and found his mother mowing the

Thanks for dropping by

lawn herself. She took exception to his tardiness and chased him around the garden with a broom that came down sharply across his shoulder breaking the broom handle in half! How could Susan have known such a personal story?

Before the couple married, sharing a bed gave rise to another potential haunting. On a summer's day if the couple were having a lie-in ice crystals would form on the inside of their bedroom windows as the temperature in the room dropped to below freezing. Susan explained that on the best of warm days these crystals could be seen growing like frost across the windows until such time they got out of bed! She went on to explain that she thought her future mom-in-law disapproved of their 'living in sin'!

On the day of John and Susan's wedding John's auntie helped Susan into her wedding dress. As Susan stood there in her under garments Susan felt that there was now another person in the room. At the same time Johns auntie also turned to observe the new arrival. Both women could see the faint figure of John's mom sitting on the end of her bed watching the wedding day events unfold. She sat there for several minutes, just long enough for Susan to show her wedding dress finery off before walking downstairs to the waiting car. John's auntie spoke to the ghostly figure who turned and looked directly at her and said, 'It's ok I can sleep now. I can rest'. John's auntie followed Susan down stairs where they drank a large whisky each before joining the wedding party. Susan recalls that she pointed out John's mom to him and the three of them looked up to the bedroom window to see John's mom waving them off. Susan blew her a kiss knowing she would not see her again, and she didn't.

The uncanny happenings don't stop there with this story, however. In researching the above, a last minute reschedule put the interview on a Monday. It coincidentally fell on the pearl wedding anniversary of John and Susan who got married on a Monday to avoid missing a Birmingham City football match and to save money on the registrar!

NIGHT NURSE

A young lady, now in her late twenties, recalls how she was comforted at night as a child when unwell by her adopted gran. The gran in this instance was a neighbour with no family of her own yet looked upon the children next door as her own. She was a kindly figure with a loving nature and the children who all saw her as another gran sorely missed her when she finally passed away.

But gran continued after death to love those children who had accepted her as family.

The young lady in this story tells of how she would wake up with a childhood fever only to have her forehead stroked until her mom and dad came into the room to take over care. She continued to say that if she felt unwell she would remove toys and clothes from a chair and place it by her bed so that gran could sit down and take care of her through the night.

One evening, though, remains ingrained in the memory of this young lady. She recalls how she had had a fever and her mom was with her. She had a pint glass of water by the side of the bed as her mother made her more comfortable. Suddenly mother and daughter were aware of a noise coming from the glass of water. A line was drawn around the middle of the glass and the top half broke away in quarters leaving the water standing in a column above the remaining half of the glass. Both witnesses remember seeing the water hang there for a good few seconds before falling onto the surface of the bedside table. As the water cascaded onto the floor the two quarter pieces of the glass shattered into a myriad of shards. Perhaps gran felt a little left out and wanted to feel that she was still needed!

DON'T CALL THE AMBULANCE

On a well-established street in the leafy suburbs of Birmingham neighbours had remained friends for years. Everyone was happy and had no need to move from the environment and security that had promoted a sense of community and neighbourliness. One evening an elderly lady went round to her neighbours of fifteen years, Jane and Jim, and asked if they would look after her husband as she was about to die. Jane and Jim looked at her in disbelief. She showed no signs of illness and so they said all the usual things of, 'Don't be silly' and 'You'll outlive us all.'

The elderly lady remained resolute that she was going to die so being the good neighbours they were they agreed to the task she had set them of looking after her husband when she had gone. Within a week the elderly lady passed away suddenly but peacefully and her widower husband soon went into decline. Jane and Jim set about trying to keep his spirits up and had a code of bangs on the interconnecting walls if he was ever in need of help. One bright sunny morning Jane was tidying the front bedroom of her house when suddenly a loud and urgent banging stole her from her daydream. The old man needed her so she dashed round whilst calling for an ambulance. Something told her that he needed medical attention immediately. The medics arrived and saved the elderly man from a near fatal heart attack. He was allowed back home after a few weeks and friendship continued. The old man did, though, say something that rocked Jane and Jim. He said, "Next time, don't call an ambulance. I will refuse to let them in to treat me." A short time later a repeat of the situation of a few months earlier occurred. This time, however, Jane didn't call an ambulance; she still had the old man's stern warning ringing in her ears. She went round to see what it was the old man needed but knew in her heart of hearts that this was what he wanted. As Jane found him lying in bed it was obvious he was having another heart attack and so she went to call an ambulance. The old man gathered his strength and refused vehemently to allow her to do such a thing. He then said that she shouldn't have called the ambulance before as he was ready to go and his wife was waiting for him. He then asked her to hold him. Jane could make out the outline of her old friend at the foot of the bed as the old man continued to talk to his wife. They spoke of their love for each other and how they would be together soon. Jane cried as the life ebbed away from the old man. Her old neighbour passed away in her arms as his waiting wife mouthed 'thank you' and disappeared. When the medics arrived they said that the heart attack had been a massive one from which there was no way back.

A NIGHT-WATCHMAN'S DAY IS NEVER DONE!

In an old Black Country town a supermarket that has now been converted into a furniture store is the scene of our next alleged haunting.

During the days of the site being used as a supermarket a night watchman was employed to look after the premises during times when the store was closed. This job was his life. He spent many hours above and beyond the call of duty simply because he loved being there and of having a sense of purpose.

Many years ago this gentleman suffered a fatal heart attack whilst on duty and some say that his spirit is still very much a part of the building even now in it's more recent role as a furniture store. There are the stories of staff hearing exit doors banging long after closing time and at regular intervals as if the night watchman is still on his regular hourly checks. Flashes of light have been seen as well around the store as if a torch has suddenly been shone in a dark corner. The most overwhelming and possibly undeniable aspect of this story is that the main entrances and exits have sensors to count customers in and out. The counters also time the counts for statistical purposes to monitor busy periods. Throughout the night and again at regular intervals the counters click and time the unseen footfall of what is thought to be the night watchman on patrol. No alarms ever sound and the only thing that can be heard is the click of the sensors as they record another visit from the caring gentleman. One manager at the store was about to leave the car park one evening. He had just locked and secured the premises

Patrolling the late shift

and was ready to drive off when his mobile phone went off. It was the wages office phone number that alarmed him. He went back into the building only to discover it empty of employees.

HELPING OUT WITH THE CATERING

Within the same building is an integral café where the staff is warm and friendly. On interviewing the staff several stories emerged regarding the potential haunting at this store. The CD player probably causes most amusement. Certain artists cannot

The unassuming kitchen with mobile utensils

be played as the CD player just won't operate. Other tracks are skipped or certain songs will suddenly play relevant to recent conversations.

As part of the daily regime at the end of the shift a cutlery trolley is loaded with knives and forks all wrapped with serviettes ready for the next day when the tables are freshly laid. Sometimes before the staff have left the building they have gone back into the kitchen only to find the trolley has been moved and the cutlery sorted neatly into separate draws of knives forks and spoons. Even the serviettes are piled up and neatly flattened out! Within this kitchen bin lids have been skimmed across the room and the female staff have had their hair pulled on numerous occasions by an unseen hand. One member of staff recalls leaving the kitchen to take food to a table. On her return she found that all the saucepans and strainers from the top shelf of the kitchen units were now in a neat row on the floor at the base of the unit! She said that once was bad enough but it happens on numerous occasions! Another member of staff said that they were preparing food in the kitchen alone and had various food containers on the work surface from out of the fridge. She walked out of the kitchen to the counter to deal with a query and on her return everything had been tidied away. No-one else had been in the kitchen other than her.

Another member of staff on one occasion helped the store cleaner to clean the toilets at the end of the day only to find all of the bins had been mysteriously and unexplainably placed in the middle of the toilet floor!

The cleaner has also reported being pushed away by an unseen force from doors that she is trying to open. Obviously after the night watchman has checked on maintaining security!

HOUSE SITTER

Just south of Birmingham lie many estates with their own identity and sense of community. One estate that borders green belt land did, however, cast a shadow over the lives of a young couple and their family. The estate was modern, and consisted of small closes that gave a safe environment in which to raise a family

For a number of years the family in question had had their regular caravan holiday and asked friends and neighbours to house sit for them and feed and clean out the menagerie of small animals that young families accrue. It soon became aware that people were getting reluctant to help out when the family booked its holiday. Excuses were made not to go around and suddenly the children would not play in the spare bedroom as they said that a man kept appearing in the mirrors of the wardrobe doors. The father of the family was noticing that his central heating system had to be switched to full on and yet the house always seemed bitterly cold. One night a group of neighbours got together for a drink and talk of the 'strange house' soon became the central point of debate. The owners of the property were agog to hear the story of one young couple employed to look after the house. They told the story that they would walk into the house and put the living room light on before walking into the kitchen. They would draw the curtains as well and prepare the food to feed the various pets and as they left the kitchen they would notice that the living room light had been switched off and the curtains opened. They went on to say that this happened several times a night. Sometimes they would just leave the curtains open only to find the next morning that curtains had been closed sometime during the night. Clearly this house was not a happy one and the cold spots around the property got colder and colder.

A chance meeting put the couple in contact with a local psychical worker who had a reputation for clearancing properties of spirits as well as having what was described as an uncanny knack of seeing what lies ahead and beyond.

Without visiting the property the psychic 'saw' and 'described' the kitchen in great detail and explained that he thought the previous owner, an elderly gentleman, had been found dead by the kitchen door. The young couple confirmed that this indeed had happened. He arranged to visit the property but agreed that only one of the couple know of the arrangements. This was to act as a control to see if one of the spouses could detect significant change after the visit. It was arranged that the lady of the house be at home.

On the agreed day and time the psychic presented himself at the property and immediately felt the chill that so many had spoken about but of which he had not been forewarned. 'Ah the chill of spirit', he extoled as he explained his actions and comments to the owner. He continued around the house checking each area of the property and soon said to the owner that much of the happenings were centred in one space. It was a locked workroom on the ground floor and he asked for it to be opened. As soon as the door was unlocked he described a howling wind blowing through the room. He could hear the voice of the elderly gentleman calling a name. He passed the name onto the lady who stood behind him and couldn't believe what was going on. The psychic repeatedly asked to whom this name belonged. It transpired it was the name of the elderly gentleman's daughter. The psychic went on to explain that he needed to help this man to pass over as his emotions wouldn't let him as he had never said goodbye to his daughter. Several minutes passed as the psychic communicated with the disturbed spirit of this man when suddenly the whole house fell still and silent.

After a cup of tea the house began to feel warmer and the psychic left the house leaving the owner somewhat bemused. That evening the psychic had a phone call from the father of the family. He simply said, "I know you were here today. I've turned my central heating down for the first time and my children are playing happily. Thank you!"

OLD NICK

The old police station in Tipton, now sadly demolished, was made from the traditional blue engineering brick that had been the favoured building material of many a factory and many a home. It held a police court in one of the upstairs rooms for minor affrays and infringements. Its holding cells were for short term containment. Ghost stories of the old nick are still spoken about locally. It appears that the main 'target' of the ghostly happenings referred to were WPC's, though generally most officers regularly witnessed 'strange episodes'. The sounds of windows slamming and the unexplainable appearance of 'footprints' were commonly reported. In 1994 a newspaper article claimed that an officer had heard footsteps in the courtroom that had been closed off almost thirty years earlier. One WPC saw the face of an out-of-the-ordinary character appearing several times at a window. When she went to check who was there the figure disappeared.

Others would put a lot of the noises down to an old heating system cooling down in the dead of night. But whose face and footprints had so clearly been witnessed by a young WPC? We shall never know.

A COLD WELCOME FOR THE VISITORS

A young professional couple moved into their new house in the late 1960's. They settled in and the property was conveniently situated for work and leisure. Everything was fine and the new house was everything it had promised to be. After a few months the lady in the house woke up suddenly one night. It was the early hours of the morning and she felt very short of breath. As she opened her eyes a dark shape retreated from her. For the rest of the night she remained uneasy from the terrifying ordeal. The couple decided to move the bed and things settled down until she had a visit from her in-laws!

The in-laws had come to stay for a few days so the master bedroom was made available to them. The happenings of a few months ago were now a distant, yet still unnerving, episode but not considered when putting the in-laws into the same room.

Next morning daughter and mom-in-law met over breakfast and soon the conversation turned to whether or not a comfortable night had been experienced. Mom-in-law said suddenly, "I didn't know you had a ghost!" She went on to explain that around two am she had awoken to her hair standing on end and the temperature in the room being freezing cold. She said she could make out a young woman in her late teens leaving the room through an open door towards the bathroom. Shortly afterwards the girl entered the bedroom again and sat on the bed. The bed visibly 'dipped' as if someone was placing their weight on the bed. As she did this the girl leaned across and stared intently into her face before disappearing. As the story unfolded the conversation turned to the apparition appearing regularly through the living room windows that looked out towards the back gate. The mystery deepened until out of the blue an elderly neighbour confided in a story about a previous owner of the property. She said how much of a pity it was that they had lost their teenage daughter to the ravages of tuberculosis.

High on the hill stands Dudley Castle

A FISHY TALE TO KEEP

Dudley Castle was built in 1070 to a motte and bailey design, fell into ruin during the Civil War and joined the list of romantic ruins. It stands atop a hill and has extensive views across a now post-industrial landscape. In its day it would have looked out over extensive woodlands and hamlets. The associated zoo was built in the castle grounds and opened in 1937.

A time and place when fish apparently just slipped away

However, in 1967 a different story was being told. A local newspaper reported that the South Staffordshire Meta-physical Society were to investigate the continuing ghostly goings on at Dudley Castle and Zoo with the aid of a tape recorder to capture some of the sounds that had been heard in the aquarium section of the zoo. Other stories surfaced as the coverage grew at this time. But it's slightly further back in time that we travel for the main story on the aquarium ghosts.

In 1953 another local paper reported upon the Birmingham Society of Psychical Research and their desire to investigate the phenomena of the 'haunted wall' and the incidences of fish vanishing without trace from the tropical temperature tanks. Icy blasts were reported as commonplace in the heated areas and to the rear of the fish tanks voices could be heard emanating from the wall

One man visiting the castle in the 1930's described how he and two other visitors were at the foot of the staircase to the castle keep. It was a quiet afternoon and all three members of the public saw an elderly couple dressed in 17th or 18th century period costume walking arm in arm. The gentleman wore a tall hat and carried a crooked walking stick. It was reported that the couple walked past the members of the public and ascended the stairs to the keep. One member of the public followed them up into the keep that was served by a single staircase and found that there was no-one there.

During October 1965 a nineteen year old youth who was employed at the castle restaurant was reported to be in 'state of shock' when he telephoned Dudley police reporting weird noises and a shape coming towards him from the keep. The youth ceased working for the restaurant as he was deeply disturbed by what he had seen. His manager suggested that the sighting his employee had witnessed was probably due to one of the white peacocks resident at the zoo. Others offer a simpler solution to the ghostly going on at the hundred-acre site: they were caused by youths merely larking about.

GHOSTS AMONG THE RUINS?

Founded by the Benedictine Order, Sandwell Priory and Holy Well were built in the late 1100's and served as a priory for a little over three hundred years.

In 1951 a local newspaper reporter was asked by a friend to take a look at some of the ghostly happenings taking place at Sandwell Priory. The reporter admitted from the outset that he was dubious about the claims of ghosts and spirits. His report is quoted as follows :

Ruined abbey plays host to an old order

'Modern physicists have declared that there can be no being without matter. I was convinced ghosts were the hallucinations of drunks or the brain projections of the imaginative.'

On a moonlit night in winter the reporter and friend made their way across the rough ground to the ruined priory. The remaining cloistered walls were remnants of Henry VIII's dissolution order when he so publically split the church in England.

Within the ruins an ancient well and pool existed which were still served by local rivers through a network of caves. The waters here were believed to have restorative properties and hence the well was known as Holy Well. The water source was described as 'bubbling away the years'.

A winter midnight silence descended bringing with it a mist as the couple walked back towards sanctity of the priory walls. Looking back towards the well the mist halted in a straight line from off the nearby roadway. As it hung and swirled it transformed itself into scowling faces and figures walking through solid walls. These cowled figures reached out to the now spooked assembly. The reporter's friend was desperate to get the camera ready to photograph the spectacle. As the figures grew nearer it was noted that the figures now had no faces at all and were merely ghostly skulls. An unearthly smell accompanied their presence as they wound their way around the site as if working at another wellhead. The silence was shattered when the reporter trod on a stick. The crack, as if amplified, drew the attention of the spirit world as the figures reached out ever closer until a blinding flash from the camera burst through the scene. This blinding light seemingly caused the mist to move and was seen disappearing over the bank towards a tree-lined pool. Shocked our two investigators went to take a drink from the well. Both instantly recoiled before scooping up the water. Splashes of water encircled the well as if someone or something had been drawing water from it. This could not be explained. The rational thoughts of a trick-of-the-eye mist were brought into crystalline sharpness that frosty night in 1951 and who could say whether this incident was real or imagination. The two people who witnessed it clearly believed it to be real as the reporter concludes in the article:

'Conscientious investigators may like to visit the Priory and make their own tests. I will furnish all the information. But I will not accompany them'.

WHAT'S IN A NAME?

A now derelict bingo hall is our next point of contact with the spirit world. A site on Walsall Street in Wednesbury was developed in March 1915 and became The Picture House. In 1938 the building was renamed and became The Gaumont. It then became The Odeon in 1964. A few years later it had another name change and became The Silver in the 1970's before changing its business from film to bingo when it became Walkers Bingo Hall where it operated for over thirty years before its closure in early 2010. With such an identity crisis over its relatively short period of operations it may come as no surprise that staff at the Bingo Hall saw plenty of ghostly happenings between calls!

Cinema turned bingo hall attracts full house!

An interview with an ex-employee reveals some strange stories indeed. Behind the stage area of the old cinema a staircase had to be removed following incidences of staff being pushed down the stairs by an unseen hand and force. Bingo books would be seen to float to the ground from off the balcony seating. This was when the hall was closed and empty of punters!

Artificial flowers that decorated the hall were found scattered across the floors when staff opened the hall in a morning. One lady who was alone in the toilets heard the toilet flush in an adjoining cubicle followed by the taps in the washbasins suddenly being turned on!

An elderly lady has also been seen rocking away in a chair on stage as well as a gentleman in cloak and hat evening dress walking through the foyer area. The vision was so clear that the manager on duty locked himself away in the office and it was still only teatime! It was certainly giving a whole new meaning to having 'a full house!'